This Annual belongs to Princess

EGMONT
We bring stories to life

Editor: Sally Gilbert
Art Editor: Alexandra Chamadia
Photography: Daniel Pangbourne

First published in Great Britain in 2007 by Egmont UK Limited,
239 Kensington High Street, London W8 6SA.

© Disney Enterprises, Inc.
ISBN 978 14052 3178 7
1 3 5 7 9 10 8 6 4 2
Printed in Italy.

Annual 2008

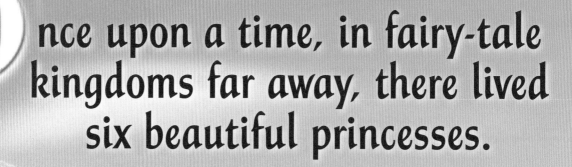

Once upon a time, in fairy-tale kingdoms far away, there lived six beautiful princesses.

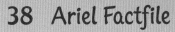

Turn the page to begin the fairy tale ...

Aurora Factfile

Read all about your favourite `sleeping beauty´.

Personality:
Very romantic.
She loves to sing.

Appearance:
Long, golden
hair with eyes the
colour of violets.

Often heard saying:
"I'm dreaming of happily
ever afters!"

Friends:
Her best friends are the
good fairies, Flora, Fauna
and Merryweather.

Princess Aurora

Magical Feelings

1 Aurora and the Prince were so happy, they never spent more than a day away from each other. "When I'm with you I feel like we're walking on air," said the Prince.

2 But the Prince got word that he would have to leave the palace for some royal business. He didn't know how long he would be away.

3 He took a rose from the garden. "When I smell the sweet scent, I'll think of you here in this happy place," he told Aurora.

4 After the Prince had been gone a few days, a cloud of loneliness descended on the palace. "Everything here misses him," sighed Aurora.

5 Aurora asked the fairies to help her send the Prince her feelings. The fairies giggled and gave Aurora an enchanted bottle.

6 Aurora used the bottle to gather the feelings of love for the Prince that came from everything around her.

7 She added her own song of love to the mixture in the enchanted bottle.

8 Aurora went to the edge of the forest and released the mixture on to the breeze. "Come home soon, my beloved prince," she whispered.

9 When the magical mixture reached the Prince, his yearning to see Aurora was so powerful that it instantly transported him home.

10 "I'll never leave you again," promised the Prince, as the magic lifted them up on a swirl of happiness. "Now we really are walking on air!" giggled Aurora.

The End

Colour in this romantic picture of Aurora and Prince Phillip.

Aurora Hairstyle

Follow these simple steps for true princess hair.

1 Wash your hair with sweet-smelling shampoo. Leave to dry naturally and then comb through.

2 Scoop the top half of your hair into a ponytail and hold it in place with a band.

3 Choose a sparkly pink hair scrunchy and carefully wrap it around the plainer band.

4 As a final princess touch, ask an adult to tie a beaded ribbon into the front of your hair.

Pretty Purses

Aurora is getting ready for a romantic evening.

Find the pink purse to go
with her outfit.

a

b

c

d

e

16

Answer:
Purse d.

What's Your Story?

Tick the hearts by the five pictures you like the most, to find your perfect story style.

Mostly pink

In your story, you would be a sweet princess, just like Aurora.

Mostly green

You are as naughty as Maleficient — your story would be full of mischief.

Mostly yellow

You would love to be the Fairy Godmothers, in a magical fairy tale.

Belle Factfile

Read all about beautiful and kind Belle.

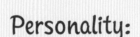

Personality:
An adventurous dreamer.

Appearance:
Pretty brown hair, with big, brown velvety eyes.

Often heard saying:
"Do the stars in my eyes show?"

Friends:
Mrs Potts, a teapot and her son Chip, a teacup. Lumiere, a candelabra and Cogsworth, a clock.

Princess Belle

A Winter's Surprise

1 It was a wintry evening. In the palace, Belle was reading a romantic book in the warm, cosy library.

2 While Belle was reading, the Beast stumbled and knocked into a bookcase. A book fell with a crash on his head.

3 "It's too dark in here," the Beast complained. "I can't find the book I want to read!" Belle had an idea.

4 "I hate the winter," the Beast growled. "It's too dark to do anything." He stormed out of the library.

5 Lumiere didn't know what to do. "I don't think that I can make myself any brighter," he fretted.

6 Belle told Lumiere not to worry. "We'll just have to make the Beast realise how nice a dark winter's evening can be," she said.

7 Belle gathered all of the Enchanted Objects and gave each of them a task. Together they created a delicious supper for the grumpy Beast.

8 A little later, Belle told the Beast she had a surprise for him in the ballroom. "It's too dark for surprises," the Beast growled.

9 But the Beast dressed for evening and followed Belle. "I suppose you've got something to do with this, too?" the Beast shouted at Cogsworth, in the hallway.

10 But the Beast was delighted when he saw the wonderful supper in the candlelit room. "We don't need bright lights to eat," Belle told him.

11 "And we don't need bright lights to dance," the Beast agreed, once they had finished their candlelit supper. They danced all night long until the sun rose.

The End

Add a pattern to Belle's ballgown and then colour it in.

23

Princess Tiara

Create this tiara - it's perfect for a princess like you!

You will need:

card

scissors

pencil

glue

jewels

sticky tape

Note to parents: adult supervision is recommended when sharp-pointed items such as scissors are in use.

1 Draw and cut out a tiara shape from thick card. Cut out areas of the tiara, too.

2 Decorate the tiara by sticking jewels on to the front. Ask an adult to position the tiara around your head and tape it in place.

Enchanted Shadows

Belle is practising her ballroom dancing.

Can you work out which is Belle's true shadow?

Answer:
Shadow c.

Royal Outfit

Roll the die and let Belle help you find
the perfect royal outfit for you.

How to play

You will need: A die. Roll a die for each panel. Look for the item that has your number next to it and tick it off. The three items together make your perfect outfit.

2 or 4 ♡   3 or 5 ♡   6 or 1 ♡

2 or 4 ♡   3 or 5 ♡   6 or 1 ♡

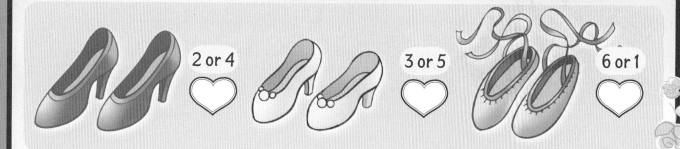

2 or 4 ♡   3 or 5 ♡   6 or 1 ♡

Cinderella Factfile

Learn all about a true fairy-tale princess - Cinderella!

Personality:
Happy, hardworking and romantic.

Appearance:
Beautiful blonde hair with clear blue eyes.

Often heard saying:
"... if you keep believing, the dreams that you wish will come true."

Friends:
Her mice friends - Gus and Jaq! And her best friend, the Fairy Godmother.

Princess Cinderella

Love in the Air

1 One day, Cinderella and the Prince were enjoying a romantic day, flying their kite.

2 Suddenly, a gust of wind took hold of the kite. "Oh, no!" exclaimed Cinderella, as she watched the kite fly through the air towards a tree.

3 Unfortunately, the kite got caught in the very top branches of the tree. It was well and truly stuck.

4 Later, Cinderella and the Prince told the Fairy Godmother what had happened. "We were having so much fun," Cinderella sighed, "and now it is all over."

5 The Fairy Godmother said she had an idea. "Time for some magic," she smiled. "Fetch me your pinkest handkerchief, Cinderella."

6 "Where are you going to find your pinkest handkerchief, Cinderelley?" questioned Gus and Jaq.

7 Cinderella knew exactly where she would find her pinkest handkerchief. "It's my wedding day handkerchief and it's full of confetti!" she laughed.

8 Cinderella gave the handkerchief to her Fairy Godmother. The Fairy Godmother waved her wand. "Now, go into the garden and there is a wonderful surprise waiting for you," she said.

9 Cinderella and the Prince ran outside and gasped, as they saw a wonderful hot-air balloon. "This is much more fun than a kite," said the Prince.

10 As they flew across the night sky in their hot-air balloon, Cinderella and the Prince felt on top of the world ... and it was the most romantic evening ... EVER!

The End

Finish colouring in this wonderful wedding day picture.

Princess Mask

Make this pretty mask for your next Princess Ball.

You will need:

pink card

glue

scissors

pencil

dowelling rod

sticky tape

feather ribbon

silver sequins

silver ribbon

1 Draw a mask shape with eye holes on some pink card and cut it out.

Note to parents: adult supervision is recommended when sharp-pointed items such as scissors are in use.

34

2 Decorate the mask with feather ribbon and lots of silver sequins.

3 Finally, decorate a dowelling rod by wrapping silver ribbon around it and gluing it in place. Attach the silver rod to the mask.

Romantic Dance

Cinderella and the Prince are at a ball.

These two pictures may look the same but there are five changes to the lower picture. Can you find them?

Answers:
Cinderella's skirt has changed colour, the Fairy Godmother's cloak has changed colour, a man is missing on the right, a musician is missing and the Prince's hair has changed colour.

Fairy-tale Fun

Test your knowledge of Cinderella with this fun quiz.

1

What did the Fairy Godmother turn a pumpkin into?

a A carriage

b A palace

c A horse

2

The stepsisters are called Anastasia and ...

a Caroline

b Drizella

c Mandy

3

What did Cinderella lose at the ball?

a A bag

b A tiara

c A slipper

Ariel Factfile

Learn some underwater facts about Ariel.

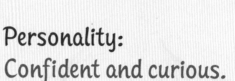

Personality:
Confident and curious.

Appearance:
Long red hair and blue-green eyes like the sea.

Often heard saying:
"It's so much fun above the waves!"

Friends:
Sebastian, a crab, and Flounder, a fish.

Princess Ariel

The Missing Sparkles

1 One day, Ariel noticed that the ocean seemed a little dull. She couldn't work out why, until she discovered a river of jewels being sucked into a cave.

2 Ariel entered the cave and found Ursula wallowing in precious stones. "Come to me my beautiful little friends," she cackled.

3 Ursula was using her magic to pull the last few jewels into the cave. "Once I own every precious stone, no one in the ocean will be richer than me," she hissed.

4 Ariel swam to tell her father. "Ursula has taken every single sparkle from the sea," she told him. "Her greed will affect the entire ocean," King Triton said, with concern.

5 "Look, it's already started," continued King Triton. "All the sea creatures are hiding, because they are scared Ursula might want them, too!"

6 "I've got to do something," said Ariel. She swam to her secret cavern to get a toy tiara she had collected. It had a loose glass bead on it.

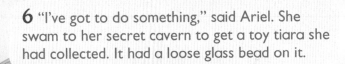

8 So Ariel swam back to find Ursula. "I have a jewel that is worth more than all of yours put together," said Ariel. "Why didn't my magic pick it up?" Ursula quizzed, suspiciously.

7 Ariel went to King Triton to tell him her plan. King Triton thought Ursula was probably greedy enough to fall for it.

9 "Because this jewel is rarer than rare and beyond any magic," replied Ariel. "I must have it," said Ursula, overpowered by her own greed.

10 "OK! I'll swap it for all the other jewels you have," said Ariel. Ursula agreed, thinking Ariel rather stupid, and swam off triumphantly.

11 While Ursula admired her worthless glass bead, Ariel returned all the jewels. "Putting the sparkle back into the sea is fun!" Ariel cheered, as she and Flounder slid around the ocean on a river of jewels!

The End

Use your prettiest pens to colour in this picture of
Ariel, Sebastian and Flounder.

Sea-Jewel Ring

Make and wear this sea-jewel ring – it's so sweet!

You will need:

card

glue

jelly sweet

sequins

sticky tape

scissors

red glitter

Note to parents: adult supervision is recommended when sharp-pointed items such as scissors are in use.

Ariel says:

Remember, the sweets are for decoration only – not for eating.

44

1 Cut a circle from card. Glue a jelly sweet to the centre and cover it with red glitter. Decorate the edge of the card with sequins.

2 Cut a strip from the card and bend into a band that will fit around your finger. Glue the band to the back of the card circle for a wonderful ring.

45

Underwater Fun

Can you help Ariel sort the six objects into pairs?

Which is the odd one out?

Answer:
The clock is the odd one out.

Colouring Game

These princesses all need a touch of colour.
Complete your picture to win the game.

How to play (2 or 3 players)

First, decide who will colour which princess. Then take it in turns to throw a die. Each time a player throws a six they colour in a section of their picture. The first player to finish their picture is the winner.

47

Snow White Factfile

Read about the fairest beauty in the land.

Personality:
Sweet, graceful and kind.

Appearance:
Black hair tied with a red ribbon. Soft, gentle brown eyes.

Often heard saying:
"One day my prince will come!"

Friends:
The seven dwarfs. She also has many woodland friends who help her.

Princess
Snow White

Butterfly Dreams

1 One morning, Snow White woke up smiling. She had just had the most fantastic dream about some beautiful butterflies.

2 Snow White went into the forest to find the butterflies. "Please come out to play," she called. But she could not find them anywhere.

3 Later, she asked the dwarfs to help her find the butterflies. The dwarfs were only too happy to help ... well, all except Grumpy! "We have too many chores to do!" he said.

4 Happy drew a picture of a butterfly to attract the butterflies ... but nothing happened. "Thank you for trying," Snow White smiled.

5 Sleepy decided to bake a berry pie ... he thought the smell might attract the butterflies. "Who's going to do the washing while you bake that silly pie?" Grumpy grumbled.

6 Doc and Bashful played some music to attract the butterflies. "Oh, well," said Snow White, when no butterflies appeared.

7 Sneezy did an impression of a butterfly to entice the butterflies, with no luck. "Thanks for trying," said Snow White, sadly.

8 Later, Snow White found Grumpy sulking in his room. "There are too many chores to do ... we should stop looking for your butterflies," he said.

9 After Snow White had spoken to the other dwarfs, they agreed to do the washing and look for the butterflies at the same time.

10 While they did their washing, Doc spoke sternly to Grumpy. "These butterflies mean so much to Snow White," he said. "Stop giving her a hard time and being so selfish!"

11 As Sneezy and Dopey hung up one of Snow White's gowns to dry, Sneezy let out a gigantic sneeze and accidentally covered the gown in red petals.

12 Sheepishly, they showed Snow White her gown. "I'm sorry we ruined it," they said. "Well, I think it looks very pretty and I'm going to put it on," said Snow White.

13 No sooner had she put on the gown, than the wonderful butterflies appeared. "They are attracted to the petals!" smiled Snow White. "So Grumpy was right to make us do the washing, after all!" Everyone laughed!

The End

Use your brightest pens and pencils to colour
in Snow White and her furry friend.

Rose Jewel-Box

Make a rose jewel-box for your princess dressing table.

1 Neatly, cover a tea box with pink felt.

2 Wrap a long length of ribbon around the box and tie it into a bow, as shown.

3 Glue fabric roses to the top of the box in any princess pattern you wish. Fill your jewel-box with your most precious things.

Dancing Birds

Snow White and the Prince are dancing in the forest.

Are there more yellow birds than
blue and yellow birds?

Write the total in the boxes below:

Answers:
No, there are more blue and yellow birds. There are seven yellow
birds, and eight blue and yellow birds.

Royal Truths

Here are some statements about Snow White.

Decide whether each statement is true or false.

1 Snow White was poisoned by an apple.

True 🤍 False 🤍

2 This is one of the dwarfs, called Grumpy.

True 🤍 False 🤍

3 This is the dwarfs' castle.

True 🤍 False 🤍

4 The Magic Mirror tells who is the fairest in the land.

True 🤍 False 🤍

Answers:
1 = True, 2 = False: it's Dopey, 3 = False: it is the dwarfs' cottage, 4 = True.

Jasmine Factfile

Read all about exotic princess ... Jasmine!

Personality:
An adventurous romantic.

Appearance:
Long black hair tied with jewelled bands, and almond-shaped brown eyes.

Often heard saying:
"A scent of roses. A dream of flying. Love is in the air!"

Friends:
Rajah, her faithful pet tiger and Aladdin!

Princess Jasmine

The Shining Palace

1 One day, as Jasmine and Aladdin walked through the market, they couldn't help noticing how sad everyone seemed to be.

2 The stall-holders and customers were all in bad moods. They shouted at each other for the silliest reasons.

3 "Maybe you can find out what's wrong and cheer everyone up?" Aladdin challenged Jasmine.

4 In the distance, Jasmine saw the towers of her father's palace. "They're so dirty that they make everything seem dull," she told Aladdin. "No wonder everyone's so gloomy!"

5 In fact, the whole street needed cleaning. Jasmine walked back to the palace with a sparkly plan in mind.

6 In her bedroom, Jasmine selected a bottle full of sparkling sequins that she had once used to decorate a dress.

7 She mixed the shiny sequins together with some soap in a huge bowl. The mixture smelt wonderful and sparkled with the sequins.

8 Then, Jasmine asked Aladdin for a favour. "We'll need to use the Magic Carpet," she told him.

9 Jasmine and Aladdin flew through the sky on the Magic Carpet. Jasmine sprinkled her glittering mix over the palace and the streets all around.

10 Suddenly, everything sparkled and glowed with colour. The towers of the palace gleamed so brightly that they lit up the sky.

11 Aladdin was very impressed. "Everything is so brightly coloured and shiny," he told Jasmine. "It's impossible not to feel happy."

12 He was right – everyone was much happier in the bright streets. "To think, I only came to the market to buy new slippers," Jasmine laughed to Aladdin.

The End

Finish colouring in Jasmine and Aladdin
on their magical adventure.

Flower Brooch

Make Jasmine's flower brooch – it's fit for a princess!

You will need:

card

pencil

scissors

plastic flowers

sticky tape

safety pin

ribbon

1 Roll the card into a cone shape, as shown, and glue in position.

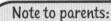

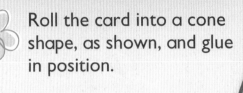

Note to parents: adult supervision is recommended when sharp-pointed items such as scissors are in use.

64

2 Glue the plastic flowers inside the cone shape, so they poke out of the top.

3 Tie a bow around the cone with a ribbon. Attach a safety pin to the back of the cone to finish your brooch.

Arabian Ball

Jasmine is getting dressed for a ball at the palace.

Can you follow the lines to see which outfit she chooses?

a

b

c

Answer:

Outfit b.

Palace Race

Can you help Jasmine reach the Sultan's palace?

A game to play with two friends.

You will need: three counters and a die. Place the counters at the start. Take it in turns to throw a die. Each time a player throws an even number, 2, 4, 6, they move forwards one space. The first player to reach the palace is the winner.

Princess Trivia

With a pencil, draw lines to match the correct princess with the
following clues and find out if you are a true princess fan.

Aurora

Cinderella

Ariel

Jasmine

Belle

Snow White

1 I went to live at the dwarfs'
cottage in the forest.

2 I have two stepsisters called
Anastasia and Drizella.

3 I love flying on the Magic
Carpet with Aladdin.

4 I was put under a spell and slept
for a hundred years.

5 I live with the Beast at his
enchanted castle.

6 I have five princess sisters.

Answers:
1 = Snow White, 2 = Cinderella, 3 = Jasmine, 4 = Aurora, 5 = Belle, 6 = Ariel.

ADVERTISEMENT

Have you seen Disney's Princess magazine?

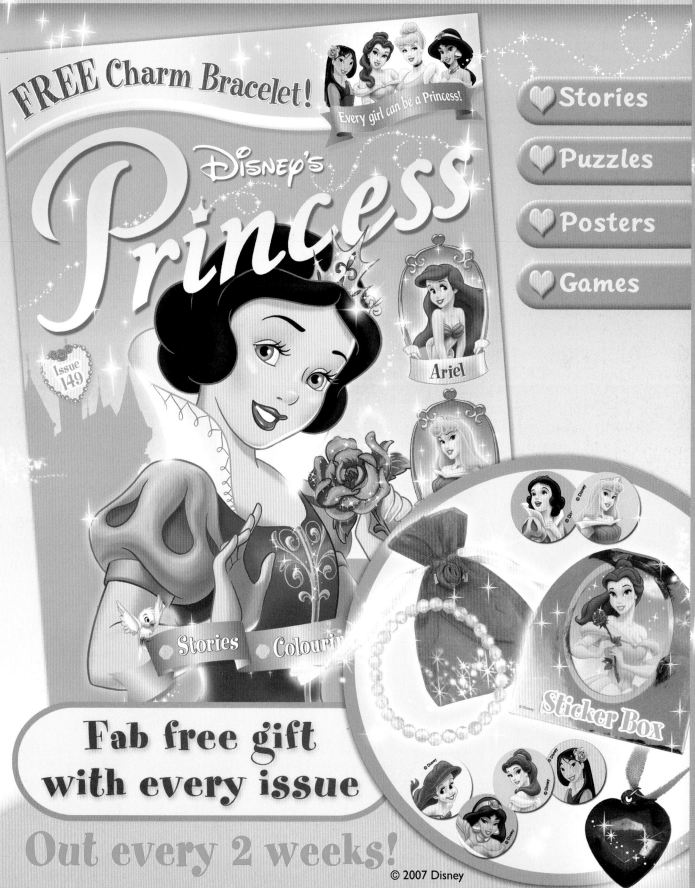